hand are unfailingly reliable. The pine cone that hangs from a nail outside my door is a dependable friend, opening up when the weather is set fair, and closing when rain is on the way. The wood anemone, likewise, always closes at the approach of rain, which also causes bees to disappear into their nests and flies to become lazy and soporific. Other insects such as ants and spiders, as well as kestrels, crows and swallows, all have patterns of behaviour which consistently provide useful information.

As for how plants and animals sense changes in the weather, that remains a mystery. Perhaps in time science will provide an explanation, and of course until there is one some people will scoff at the whole idea, as they always do at things they don't understand. My view is that we should be humble enough to accept that there *are* some things that we don't understand – perhaps will never understand, though I hope there will be some serious scientific research into this before long. Didn't the philosopher say that true wisdom lies in knowing how little we know?

I for one will never tire of observing my surroundings, and accepting the wisdom our ancestors have handed down to us and the tips that Nature in her generosity offers to those who are prepared to look.

Bill Foggitt
Thirsk, North Yorkshire, March 1992

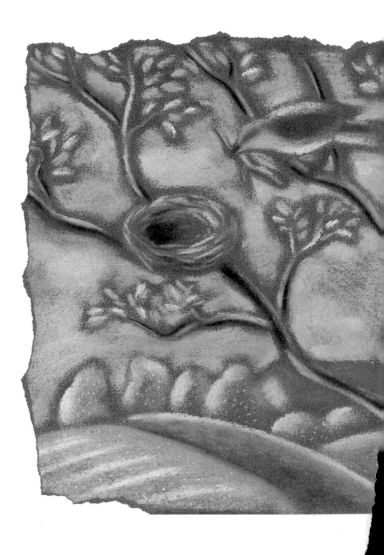

WEATHERWISE

FACTS, FICTIONS AND PREDICTIONS

great gales, severe droughts and brilliant auroral displays. I took over in 1968, following on from my uncle, my father and my brother. Having retired from active work in 1966 owing to a road accident, I have had ample opportunity to study the weather from the angle of Nature, and I look forward to doing so for some time yet.

I often refer back to my records from earlier years and spot patterns which, together with the indicators our ancestors relied on, help me to make forecasts – and, without wishing to boast, sometimes more accurate ones than my well-paid colleagues on the television and radio!

I cannot help noticing that the professional forecasters often seem to be better at telling us what sort of weather we've had today than what it will be like tomorrow. I am not suggesting that they are only any good at being wise after the event.

I should add that scientific forecasting has come a long way, and nowadays they have a tremendous range of technology to call on. In addition to a network of weather ships, planes and often remote weather stations, there are radar scanners which can pick up clouds and belts of rain over a hundred miles away, radio sondes measuring temperature, humidity and pressure at heights of over twenty miles, and satellites, either stationary or in orbit, scanning the earth's surface and sending back pictures of cloud patterns and depressions. No wonder the public expect to be told about hurricanes before they happen!

Methods of presenting weather information and forecasts have also become very sophisticated and complicated – so much so that I reckon many viewers, like me, probably don't understand half of what they see on the weather charts. Perhaps that is why I'm finding that there's more and more interest in traditional methods of weather forecasting, from members of the public and, increasingly, the media.

People often come and ask me which are the

most reliable weather indicators, and how much truth there is in the old rhymes and sayings. In my experience, all the signs included in this book have definite value, although a few need to be treated with caution because, as I have noted, they only hold good under certain conditions or in certain parts of the world. Some on the other

WEATHERWISE

FACTS, FICTIONS AND PREDICTIONS

BILL FOGGITT

Illustrations by Walter van Lotringen

PAVILION

First published in Great Britain in 1992 by
PAVILION BOOKS LIMITED
196 Shaftesbury Avenue, London WC2H 8JL

Designed by Charles Barr

A CIP catalogue record for this book is
available from the British Library

ISBN 1 85145 9561

Printed in Great Britain by Bath Press Colourbooks, Glasgow

2 4 6 8 10 9 7 5 3

This book may be ordered by post direct from
the publisher. Please contact the Marketing
Department. But try your bookshop first.

CONTENTS

INTRODUCTION
6

SPRING
10

SUMMER
30

AUTUMN
50

WINTER
66

INTRODUCTION

The weather never ceases to fascinate me, and I suppose I have been studying it for upwards of seventy years. When I was a boy, there was no radio or television, and the main recreation for my brother, my sister and me was going on country walks with our parents. They taught us to use our eyes, to spot the tell-tale weather signs in the lives of plants, animals and insects, and by our own observations to test the accuracy of the traditional weather sayings, many of which I have collected in this book.

The weather, of course, has always been studied closely, and not just by farmers, for whom it can be a matter of life and death. It has also inspired some of the finest poetry and prose in the English language, and I have included a number of personal favourites.

You will also find here an amazing range of facts about the weather: record-breaking extremes of heat and cold, rainfall, snowfall, wind speed and so on, as well as extraordinary events, some strange, some disastrous, some even humorous.

An interest in the weather and weather lore goes back a long way in our family. From 1880 to 1906, my grandfather William Foggitt, a botanist, kept a daily log of the weather, which has been continued by his descendants to the present day. Our records include accounts of

Spring

SPRING

Spring is a time of celebration. The dark days of winter are drawing out, buds form on trees and hedges, the first wild flowers begin to appear, there's warmth in the sun, and the birds sing merrily. No wonder, then, that poets writing about the spring often sound as frisky as spring lambs. 'Cuckoo, jug-jug, pu-we, to-witta-woo!'

For the farmer, however, it's a deadly serious time of year. The decisions he makes now, about what and when to sow, are crucial to his livelihood, and the weather from spring onwards can either help him or undo all his work. A downpour shortly after sowing may wash away his seed; a hard late frost may kill off his tender seedlings. He is also looking ahead to the summer, knowing when he needs rain to fill out his grain, fruit or vegetables, and sun to ripen them, and when he least wants wind or rain – at harvest time. Hail, of course, is never welcome. In the USA alone, hail causes crop damage to the tune of about a billion dollars a year. If only the famer could predict the pattern of the year's weather, he could plan accordingly, resigning himself in poor years to growing those crops best able to survive. This may be why so many of the springtime weather sayings relate to long-term trends and the likely outcome of the weather conditions experienced in March and April.

A peck of March dust is worth a king's ransom.
A dry March means that the newly sown seed
will not be washed away, and the farmer can
expect a good crop.

So many mists in March you see,
So many frosts in May will be.

Mists in March come with east winds off the
North Sea, and when the wind is easterly in
March it often stays on into May, when east
winds bring frosts.

*When March comes in like a lion it goes
out like a lamb.*

April showers bring May flowers.
Showers in April are welcomed by farmers
and gardeners. Wind, too, is regarded
as a good sign.

The wood anemone is a useful weather
forecaster. Flowering at the end of March or the
beginning of April, it is a natural barometer,
closing its petals at the approach of rain.

Swallows and martins usually arrive around
the middle of April. If they arrive earlier,
this indicates a fine summer. The later they
arrive, the shorter and more unsettled the
summer will be.

*If the oak's before the ash,
Summer then will be a splash.
If the ash is before the oak,
Summer then will be a soak.*

The oak nearly always comes into leaf before
the ash. In an exceptionally cold spring such as
1962, however, they have been known to
burgeon at the same time.

When April blows his horn
'Tis good for hay and corn.

Quito, in Ecuador, claims to have the best climate in the world. Known as 'the land of eternal spring', it receives about 4ins (100mm) of rain a month; the temperature rises to 72°F (22°C) in the daytime, and never falls below 46°F (8°C) at night.

The Great Plains area of the USA is called 'Tornado Alley'. It is the world's greatest tornado factory. The USA experiences about 770 tornadoes a year. In April 1974, a group of around 148 tornadoes killed 315 people in the Mid-West and caused $600,000,000 in damage.

The greatest rainfall ever recorded in a 24-hour period is 73.62ins (1,870mm), at Cilaos, on the island of Réunion in the Indian Ocean near Madagascar, on 15-16 March 1952.

The highest recorded speed ever reached by a tornado is 280mph (450kmph), measured during the tornado which struck Wichita Falls, Texas, on 2 April 1958.

The greatest loss of life caused by a tornado occurred in 1925. In just 3 hours on 18 March a tornado killed 689 people in the southern central USA.

On 21 May 1950 a tornado travelled nearly 100 miles (160km) across England to Blakeney, on the Norfolk coast. The distance is a British record for a tornado, and the trail of damage left by its 4-hour journey included roofless houses, twisted television aerials and a number of chickens plucked completely bare.

Spring, the sweet Spring, is the year's
pleasant king;
Then blooms each thing, then maids
dance in a ring,
Cold doth not sting, the pretty birds do sing —
Cuckoo, jug-jug, pu-we, to-witta-woo!

The palm and may make country houses gay,
Lambs frisk and play, the shepherds pipe all day,
And we hear aye birds tune this merry lay —
Cuckoo, jug-jug, pu-we, to-witta-woo!

The fields breathe sweet, the daisies
kiss our feet,
Young lovers meet, old wives a-sunning sit,
In every street these tunes our ears do greet —
Cuckoo, jug-jug, pu-we, to-witta-woo!
Spring, the sweet Spring!

Thomas Nash, 'Spring'

The year's at the spring
And day's at the morn;
Morning's at seven;
The hill-side's dew-pearled;
The lark's on the wing;
The snail's on the thorn:
God's in his heaven —
All's right with the world!

Robert Browning, 'The Year's at the Spring'

Britain's heaviest recorded hailstone weighed 5oz
(141g). In 1975 hailstones 'as big as golfballs'
were reported in the Midlands. The largest
hailstone found in the USA fell in Kansas in
1970. It weighed over $1\frac{1}{2}$lbs (750g) and was
$7\frac{1}{2}$ins ($17\frac{1}{2}$cm) in diameter.

Large blocks of ice have occasionally fallen from
the sky. Mysterious in origin, except when
analysis shows them to have dropped from the
wings of aircraft, they are known as ice
meteors. In Middlesex, England, a large block of
ice fell on to the roof of a car while its owner
was washing it in March 1974.
Three years later, just a few miles away, a block
of ice weighing about 110lbs (50kg) smashed
through the roof of a house and came to rest in
a bedroom.

The early appearance of frogspawn indicates a mild spring and early summer – suitable weather for tadpoles.
The position of frogspawn on a pond is also significant. If the spawn is in a sheltered spot near the edge, a wet and windy spring is expected. If it is out in the middle, it indicates a dry spring and early summer. It appears that frogs choose deep water for safety when they sense impending drought.

Thunder in April, floods in May.
Thunderstorms in April bring particularly heavy showers, often leaving floods well into the following month.

Rain in May is good for hay.
The crops need plenty of moisture to grow.

A swarm of bees in May
Is worth a load of hay.

Bees detest wet weather and will only swarm when it is settled and dry. They give ample warning of rainstorms by disappearing into their hives.

When bees crowd into the hives again,
It's a sure sign of storms and rain.

The afternoon had been stormy but it cleared
towards sunset. Gradually the heavy rain clouds
rolled across the valley to the foot of the
opposite mountains and began climbing up their
sides wreathing in rolling masses of vapour.
One solitary cloud still hung over the brilliant
sunlit town, and that whole cloud was a
rainbow. Gradually it lost its bright prismatic
hues and moved away up the Cusop Dingle in
the shape of a pillar and of the colour of golden
dark smoke. The Black Mountains were
invisible, being wrapped in clouds, and I saw
one very white brilliant dazzling cloud where
the mountains ought to have been. This cloud
grew more white and dazzling every moment,
till a clearer burst of sunlight scattered the mists
and revealed the truth. This brilliant white
cloud that I had been looking and wondering at
was the mountain in snow. The last cloud and
mist rolled away over the mountain tops and the
mountain stood up in the clear blue heaven . . .

Diary of The Rev. Francis Kilvert, 14 March 1871

Strowe me the ground with Daffadowndillies,
And Cowslips, and Kingcups, and loved Lillies:
   The pretie Pawnce,
    And the Chevisaunce,
Shall match with the fayre flowre Delice.

Edmund Spenser, 'April'

I have been loitering out in the garden here this golden day of Spring. The wood-pigeons coo in the covert; the frogs croak in the pond; the bees hum about some thyme: and some of my smaller nieces have been busy gathering primroses.

Edward FitzGerald, Letter of 3 April 1845

The world's wettest place is Tutunendo, in Colombia, which has an average annual rainfall of 463.4ins (11,770mm).

Only very slightly drier is Mount Wai-'ale-'ale, in Hawaii, with 460.00ins (11,684mm). Arguably the least promising place in the world for a game of baseball or cricket, it has rain for about 335 days of the year.

On Friday 13 November 1970 the Ganges delta in Bangladesh was hit by a tropical cyclone of devastating power. Winds of 120mph (192kmph), torrential rain and a massive tidal wave caused loss of life estimated at anything up to 1,000,000. Most of the victims drowned, and many thousands were never found.

It is estimated that 10 per cent of the earth's surface has less than 9.8ins (250 mm) of rain a year.

Hurricanes can blow paths of destruction 400 miles (645km) wide. Their winds circulate around an *eye*, between 5 and 25 miles (8 and 40 km) across. Fortunately, they take days or weeks to form, so there is time to prepare for them. When they hit land they uproot trees, tear down power lines and cause serious injuries.

It has been raining, softly and silently, a benevolent rain, and the large red blossoms of the almonds, and the buds of the lilac, and the branches of the firs are full of that delicate day dew, glittering and glancing and shaking off showers of jewels into the moistened ground.

John Ruskin, Letter of 25 March 1836

I was so hot this morning with my walk, that I resolve to do so no more during this violent burning weather. It is comical, that now we happen to have such heat to ripen the fruit, there has been the greatest blast that was ever known, and almost all the fruit is despaired of.

Jonathan Swift, Letter of 31 May 1711

The cock is crowing,
The stream is flowing,
The small birds twitter,
The lake doth glitter,
The green field sleeps in the sun;
The oldest and youngest
Are at work with the strongest;
The cattle are grazing,
Their heads never raising;
There are forty feeding like one!
Like an army defeated
The snow hath retreated ...

William Wordsworth (written in March)

Summer

SUMMER

In summertime we seem to spend most of our time wondering whether it's ever going to rain – or else whether it's ever going to stop. The weather sayings for summer mostly reflect this. We all know those days of sultry, distracting heat, the kind of thundery heat which causes milk to go sour, cows to leap over gates, and poets to wander off into woods to alter their poems. And we know the sense of relief which comes when a storm finally breaks, and rain refreshes the whole landscape – Wordsworth's exuberant hare, raising his plume of spray, captures the mood perfectly. Often, however, the rain outstays its welcome, as it apparently once did in the ninth century, giving rise to one of the more dubious weather sayings.

St Swithin, a bishop of Winchester, died in 862 and was buried in a churchyard, as he had wished. A century later it was decided to move his remains to more dignified surroundings inside Winchester Cathedral. This, it seems, angered the spirit of St Swithin, who made it rain so heavily for the next forty days that the plan was abandoned. As the saying is almost certainly based on legend, not observation, perhaps we should take it with a pinch of salt. Weather diaries are full of exceptions to the rule. I have included it because it has such an established place in weather lore.

Mists in May, heat in June
Makes the harvest come right soon.

A sunny June keeps things in tune.

Lazy fly, rain is nigh.
When flies cling to us, especially in warm,
sultry weather, rain is close at hand.

Swift moves the Ant as the mercury rises.
As the temperature rises it is noticeable that
ants move much more quickly.

When spiders spin long radial strands in their
webs, a spell of dry weather can be expected.
It appears that when spiders can sense dry
weather coming they have the confidence to
build wide, flimsy webs. When wet or windy
weather is on the way, like a sailor shortening
his sail they spin short strands.

St Swithin's Day if thou dost rain,
For forty days it will remain.
St Swithin's Day if thou be fair,
For forty days it will rain no more.

St Swithin's Day is 15 July.

A good short-term weather forecaster is the
Scarlet Pimpernel, the roadside flower known
as 'the poor man's weatherglass'. When its
petals begin to close, rain is in the offing; when
they are wide open, fine weather is set to
continue.

Hens will often take shelter just before
rain commences, and come out again just
before it stops.

The hottest place on earth, with an average
annual temperature in the shade of 94°F
(34.4°C), is Dallol, in Ethiopia's northern
desert, once known as the Hot Lands
of Abyssinia.

In 1946 there were only about 4 weeks of
chilly weather at Wyndham, Western Australia.
On 333 days of the year, temperatures of 90°F
(32.2°C) were recorded.

Death Valley, California, lived up to its name in
1917. On 43 consecutive days, from 6 July to
17 August, maximum temperatures of over
120°F (48.9°C) were recorded.

Britain's highest ever temperature in the shade
is 98.2°F (36.77°C), measured on 9 August
1911 in the counties of Surrey, Kent and
Northamptonshire.

The world record for shade temperature is
136.4°F (58°C), at al'Aziziyah, in Libya, on
13 September 1922.

The driest place in the world is the Desierto de
Atacama, near Calama in Chile, where the
average annual rainfall is given as nil.

Not surprisingly, the Desierto de Atacama also
holds the record for the world's longest
drought. The rain which fell there in 1971
is believed to have been the first for about
400 years.

July passed over their heads, and the
Thermidorean weather which came in its wake
seemed an effort on the part of Nature to
match the state of hearts at Talbothays Dairy.
The air of the place, so fresh in the spring and
early summer, was stagnant and enervating now.
Its heavy scents weighed upon them, and at
mid-day the landscape seemed lying in a swoon.
Ethiopic scorchings browned the upper slopes of
the pastures, but there was still bright green
herbage here where the water-courses purled.
And as Clare was oppressed by the outward
heats, so was he burdened inwardly by waxing
fervour of passion for the soft and silent Tess.
The rains having passed, the uplands were dry.
The wheels of the dairyman's spring cart, as he
sped home from market, licked up the
pulverised surface of the highway, and were
followed by white ribands of dust, as if they
had set a thin powder-train on fire. The cows
jumped wildly over the five-barred barton-gate,
maddened by the gad-fly; Dairyman Crick kept
his shirt-sleeves permanently rolled up from
Monday to Saturday; open windows had no
effect in ventilation without open doors, and in
the dairy-garden the blackbirds and thrushes
crept about under the currant-bushes, rather in
the manner of quadrupeds than of winged
creatures. The flies in the kitchen were lazy,
teasing, and familiar, crawling about in
unwonted places, on the floor, into drawers,
and over the backs of the milkmaids' hands.

Thomas Hardy, Tess of the d'Urbervilles

Intensely hot. William went into the wood, and
altered his poems.

Diary of Dorothy Wordsworth, 28 July 1800

In both Britain and the USA there have been
numerous reports of frogs or small fish falling
from the sky in large quantities – confusing for
all concerned. On 16 June 1939 a shower of
tiny frogs fell on Trowbridge, Wiltshire,
England, probably having been lifted from their
ponds by a small tornado or freakish upcurrent.

The most catastrophic droughts in American history were those experienced in the central plains during the 1930s, creating the notorious Dust Bowl. The drought of 1930-31 lasted a full year, and further droughts occurred in the area every year until 1940. The soil became so dry that it was blown away by the wind, and farmers were wiped out.

The terrible scale of the destruction caused by the Great Fire of London was partly caused by drought. London had had a hot summer and virtually no rain for over a year, and the wooden buildings of the city were as dry as tinder when the fire started on 2 September 1666. The flames spread rapidly, and the fire raged out of control for three days and nights. A week later, ironically, the drought ended, and early in October there was a 10-day period of continuous heavy rain – which could have saved the city.

The world record for the number of thunder days per year is held by Tororo, in Uganda, with an average annual total of 251 days.

Rainbows seldom appear for long, but on 14 August 1979 a rainbow was seen on the coast of North Wales which lasted for three hours – probably a world record.

Lightning never strikes twice.
Let's just say it's unusual for the same place to
be struck more than once. A church at Boston
Spa in Lincolnshire, England, has been struck
by lightning 152 times, and the Empire State
Building in New York City is hit on average 23
times a year.

Beware the oak,
It draws the stroke;
Avoid the ash,
It draws the flash;
But under the thorn
You'll come to no harm.

Tall trees attract flashes of lightning. It is safer
to shelter under a low thorn bush.

If St Bartholomew's Day is dry and clear,
There'll be a good autumn in that year.

St Bartholomew's Day is 25 August.

A build-up of billowy white cumulus clouds
gives warning of approaching thunderstorms,
often the same day:

Mountains in the morning,
Fountains in the evening.

I bring fresh showers for the thirsting flowers,
From the seas and the streams;
I bear light shade for the leaves when laid
In their noonday dreams.
From my wings are shaken the dews that waken
The sweet buds every one,
When rocked to rest on their mother's breast,
As she dances about the sun.
I wield the flail of the lashing hail,
And whiten the green plains under,
And then again I dissolve it in rain,
And laugh as I pass in thunder.

Percy Bysshe Shelley, 'The Cloud'

There was a roaring in the wind all night;
The rain came heavily and fell in floods;
But now the sun is rising calm and bright;
The birds are singing in the distant woods;
Over his own sweet voice the
Stock-dove broods;
The Jay makes answer as the Magpie chatters;
And all the air is filled with pleasant noise
of waters.

All things that love the sun are out of doors;
The sky rejoices in the morning's birth;
The grass is bright with rain-drops; –
on the moors
The Hare is running races in her mirth;
And with her feet she from the plashy earth
Raises a mist; that, glittering in the sun,
Runs with her all the way, wherever she
doth run.

William Wordsworth, 'The Leech-gatherer'

Milk will sometimes turn sour when a thunderstorm is close at hand. Thunderstorms are more likely to occur during sultry weather, which accelerates the development of the bacteria that turn milk sour.

Heatwaves end in thunderstorms.

A rainbow can indicate the approach of either good or bad weather, depending on the time of day it appears:

Rainbow at morn,
Good weather has gone.

Here the rainbow is in the west, and the sun is shining on drops of moisture approaching from the west. Rain is coming.

Rainbow after noon,
Good weather comes soon.

A rainbow after midday must be in the east, with the sun in the west. The rain has gone.

A rare but reliable weather forecaster is the house cricket. A member of the grasshopper family, easily recognizable by its long antennae, it chirps at night when rain is on the way.

One of Britain's worst flood disasters occurred
in North Devon in August 1952. Over 30
people were killed and over 300 left homeless.
In the USA in 1889 a flood in Johnstown,
Pennsylvania, killed 2,200 people.

On 18 August 1974, numerous waterspouts were observed off the south coast of England. Waterspouts form when tornadoes occur over lakes or oceans. Clouds of spray are torn up from the surface by the violent updrafts and form tall, whirling columns.

The highest waterspout ever recorded in British waters was seen off Ryde, Isle of Wight, on 21 August 1878. Its height, measured by sextant, was about 2,000ft (600m).

In 1898 a waterspout which appeared off Eden, New South Wales, Australia, was measured by theodolite to be 5,014ft (1,528m) high. This remains the highest of all reliably recorded waterspouts.

Autumn

AUTUMN

Some weather sayings are only partly true. Patterns of behaviour also vary from place to place, so a well verified local sign is as reliable as anything.

My cat Blackie dashes about with his tail in the air to warn me that I should batten down the hatches because it's going to be windy – though whether all cats perform this excellent service I wouldn't like to say. There are numerous claims about cats predicting the weather. Some say that a cat sneezing or washing its ears is a sign of rain. There is a tradition in Cambridge, Massachusetts, that when a cat's fur looks unusually shiny it indicates that the next day's weather will be fine. In Eastern Massachusetts they reckon that the face of a washing cat always points in the direction from which the wind will blow; whereas in Western Maine they say that when a cat is sharpening its claws, its tail will be pointing in the direction from which it will blow the following day. In Central Maine there is an even more surprising claim: that the mere fact of a cat looking out of a window is a sign of impending storm. In my experience cats spend a great deal of their time looking out of windows, and I have my doubts. Perhaps I should put it to Blackie, who knows these things, but I fear I would only get one of his withering looks.

What July and August were unable to boil,
September and October will scarcely be able to fry.

When land and sea have been cooled down
during a cold, wet summer, no amount of sun in
the following months will make up for it.

September either dries up ditches or
breaks down bridges.

September rainfall tends to be extremely low or
extremely high, leading to drought or flood.

A kestrel hovering low over the ground indicates
showery and blustery weather to come.
He is anxiously hunting for mice before the
weather deteriorates.

When rooks and gulls twirl high in the sky
It's a certain sign that a gale is nigh.

🍂

Shortly before a cold spell you may see a mouse
in the house.

🍂

While rain depends, the pensive cat gives o'er
Her frolics, and pursues her tail no more.

So Jonathan Swift wrote, over two hundred
years ago. It is also said that by walking with its
tail up, a cat indicates approaching wind; and if
it scratches the table legs, there will be a
change in the weather.

🍂

Swallows usually leave the north of England
during the first few days of October. If they
leave before that, it's a sign of an early winter.

🍂

The days around St Luke's Day, 8 October, are
usually fine and mild in England. This interlude
is known as St Luke's Little Summer.

🍂

Evening red and morning glory
Sets the traveller on his way.
Evening grey and morning red
Brings down showers on his head.

Dull November brings a blast.
Hark the leaves are falling fast.

Manchester, England, has the reputation for being one of the rainiest places in a rainy country. This is an injustice; its average annual rainfall of 32.3ins (819mm) is between those of Venice, with 30.3ins (770mm), and Rome, with 36.0ins (915mm).

❧

The largest hailstone ever recorded fell on 14 April 1986 in Bangladesh, weighing 2.25lbs (1.02kg). The hailstorm killed 92 people at Gopalganj.

❧

The largest hailstone ever recorded in the USA fell at Coffeyville, Kansas, on 3 September 1970. It weighed 1.67lbs (758g) and had a diameter of 7.5ins (190mm) and a circumference of 17.5ins (444mm). The storm caused widespread damage to houses and crops.

❧

On 5 September 1958, large hailstones, some as big as tennis balls, fell on a village in Sussex, southern England, destroying an entire 50-acre apple crop on one farm alone.

❧

In September 1928, 6,000 people died when a hurricane devastated areas of the West Indies and Florida. In October 1963, the same number were killed in Cuba and Haiti by Hurricane Flora.

The worst storm in British history was probably
the Great Storm of 1703. Details of the
destruction caused to hundreds of ships, houses,
churches and windmills and tens of thousands of
trees were compiled by Daniel Defoe, collating
reports from all over the country. The storm
began on 26 November and grew more violent
in the early hours of the 27th. An estimated
8,000 people died, many of them on board the
12 men-o'-war which were wrecked on the
Goodwin Sands. The Eddystone lighthouse and
all inside it disappeared without trace.

Season of mists and mellow fruitfulness,
Close bosom-friend of the maturing sun;
Conspiring with him how to load and bless
With fruit the vines that round the
thatch-eves run;
To bend with apples the moss'd cottage trees,
And fill all fruit with ripeness to the core;
To swell the gourd, and plump the hazel shells
With a sweet kernel; to set budding more,
And still more, later flowers for the bees,
Until they think warm days will never cease,
For Summer has o'er-brimm'd their
clammy cells.

Where are the songs of Spring? Ay,
where are they?
Think not of them, thou hast thy music too, —
While barrèd clouds bloom the soft-dying day,
And touch the stubble-plains with rosy hue;
Then in a wailful choir the small gnats mourn
Among the river sallows, borne aloft
Or sinking as the light wind lives or dies;
And full-grown lambs loud bleat
from hilly bourn;
Hedge-crickets sing; and now with treble soft
The red-breast whistles from a garden-croft;
And gathering swallows twitter in the skies.

John Keats, 'To Autumn'

One of the most destructive storms in American history was the hurricane which roared in from the Atlantic unexpectedly on 21 September 1938 and cut a swathe across New England, destroying thousands of cars and buildings and killing 389 people. The worst damage was at Westhampton, Long Island, which was hit by a massive wall of water and winds of 120mph (192kmph). One man was carried 2 miles (3.2km) inland by the flood – on the roof of his house.

The windiest place in the world is The
Commonwealth Bay, George V Coast,
Antarctica, where there are gales of up to
200mph (320kmph).

❦

A horrific and possibly unique instance of human
hailstones occurred in Germany in 1930. Five
airmen had to bail out and parachuted into a
thunderstorm over the Rhön mountains.
Bounced up and down in the cloud, they became
the centres of hailstones as layers of ice formed
around them. When they finally fell to the
ground, only one survived. The others
were frozen.

❦

A violent American tornado once acted with the
precision of a crane. A railway engine was
picked up by the tornado, turned round in the
air and neatly replaced on an adjacent track – to
continue its journey in the opposite direction.

❦

A sinister event occurred in Switzerland on 14
October 1755, when rain the colour of blood
fell on Locarno, and red snow was seen falling
on the Alps. It is believed that the dust had
been lifted from the Sahara Desert and blown
nearly 2,000 miles (3,200km) by the wind. The
same explanation was given for the red-coloured
rain which fell on parts of western Scotland on
5-6 March 1977.

Trace in the sky the painter's brush,
And winds around you soon will rush.

Wispy cirrus clouds, the highest clouds in the
sky, foretell approaching winds.

🍂

If November ice will bear a duck,
Most of winter will be slush and muck.

If there are sharp frosts in November, they are
usually followed by rain and snow in December.
On the other hand:

Much water in Autumn,
Much ice at Christmas.

🍂

My mother, well versed in weather lore
throughout her long life, quoted this saying
during the torrential downpours of September
1976. Sure enough, Christmas 1976 was frosty.

🍂

Here is another confident prediction, for those
who like their forecasts to be precise:

If ducks slide at Hallowtide,
At Christmastide the ducks will swim.
If ducks swim at Hallowtide,
At Christmastide the ducks will slide.

Hallowtide is 31 October.

We are having fine autumn weather. The harvest
is all in, and the woods are just touched with
russet, the apples weigh down the branches, the
children are blackberrying all along the lanes in
the broad light, and there is just the slight smell
of burning in the air and the light level lines of
smoke along the bottoms of the commons, that
brings such a vivid sense of change of season.
The pretty play of summer is over, and we have
to go down into the dark cavern of winter.

M. S. Holland, Letter of 12 September 1883

The fifth of October, at night happened a
terrible tempest of wind and raine both on the
sea and land by meanes whereof many ships and
other vessels drowned, about midnight the water
overflowing, drowned many meadowes, pastures,
townes, villages, cattell, houses, and goods, to
the utter undoing of a great number of subjects
of this Realme: besides the losse of many
women, and children, some drowned in their
Beds, and some as they travelled.

John Stow, Chronicle, 1570

WINTER

Some traditional lore which passes for wisdom simply isn't. Not a few country folk cling to the idea that a profusion of berries in the autumn presages a hard winter. In fact, all it shows is that there was a mild, frost free spring which permitted unrestricted pollination and fertilization.

The bitter kind of winter weather described in 'When icicles hang by the wall' by Shakespeare does not occur very often nowadays.

We have had the occasional severe winter, as witness 1947 and 1963, but some readers will be surprised to learn that in London for example there have only been seven white Christmases so far this century. Our memories about weather often deceive us, and the only way to build a clear picture of weather patterns is to keep a weather diary.

It was at Christmas, when I was about fourteen, that I received my first diary. I still have it, and I well remember my father promising me another the following Christmas if I filled in this one every day. I protested that it would be repetitive. 'Oh no,' Father replied, 'write something each day about the weather and you'll find that no two days are exactly the same weatherwise.'

How right he was. And what pleasure I have had in proving it.

Winter

When squirrels early start to hoard,
Winter will pierce us like a sword.

If the leaves stay late on the trees it is a sign of
a hard winter.

Mackerel sky,
Not long wet, not long dry.

A sky full of cirro-cumulus clouds is called a
mackerel sky because its rippling pattern
resembles the scales of a fish.

The colours in the winter sky at sunset are
indicative. Pale yellow usually means wind or
rain, or both; pale green presages snow.

Onion skin, very thin,
Mild winter coming in.

Shortly before the arrival of wet and windy weather, cattle huddle together in fields or in the shelter of hedges.

South winds surely bring us rain,
North winds blow it back again;
West winds surely bring wet weather,
East brings wet and cold together.

In hilly districts, sheep come down to the lowlands shortly before the arrival of snow.

Chill December brings the sleet,
Blazing hearth and Christmas treat.

The last of London's 'pea-souper' fogs occurred in December 1952 and killed an estimated 2,850 people. The figure represents the increased number of deaths from bronchitis and pneumonia reckoned to be attributable to the smog. It was possibly the worst fog of all time. On the Isle of Dogs, beside the Thames in east London, the fog was said to be so dense that you could not even see your own feet. Several people walked into the river. The West End also had a difficult time, theatre-goers who had successfully found their seats complaining that they couldn't see the stage.

The greatest recorded loss of life caused by avalanche occurred in northern Italy during the First World War. A series of over 100 avalanches in the Dolomite valleys on 13 December 1916 killed an estimated 10,000 Italian and Austrian soldiers. Bodies were still being found in the 1950s.

The world's coldest place, with an average
annual temperature of −72°F (−57.8°C),
is Vostok in Antarctica, known as the Pole of
Cold. It also holds the record for the lowest
temperature ever recorded: −128.6°F
(−89.2°C).

The greatest fall in temperature in one day is
100°F (55.5° C), from 44°F (6.7°C) to −56°F
(−48.8°C), recorded at Browning, Montana,
USA, on 23-24 January 1916.

I love to see the old heath's withered brake
  Mingle its crimpled leaves with furze
      and ling,
  While the old heron from the lonely lake
Starts slow and flaps his melancholy wing,
  And oddling crow in idle motions swing
On the half-rotten ash-tree's topmost twig,
Beside whose trunk the gipsy makes his bed.
Up flies the bouncing woodcock from the brig
  Where a black quagmire quakes beneath
      the tread;
The fieldfares chatter in the whistling thorn
And for the haw round fields and closen rove,
  And coy bumbarrels, twenty in a drove,
Flit down the hedgerows in the frozen plain
And hang on little twigs and start again.

John Clare, 'Emmonsail's Heath in Winter'

With my wife for half an hour walking in the
moonlight, and it being cold, frosty weather,
walking in the garden, and then home to supper,
and so by the fireside to have my head combed,
as I do now often do, by Deb.

Samuel Pepys, Diary, 11 January 1668

The difference altitude can make to air temperature was graphically demonstrated in New York City on 3 November 1958. While rain was falling on 34th Street, the guards on top of the Empire State Building, 1,150ft (350m) above ground level, were having a snowball fight.

In January 1937, the combination of a sudden
thaw and freakish levels of rainfall caused the
Ohio River to flood along its entire length.
Whole towns were submerged, and parts of
Cincinnati had flooding 80ft (24m) deep.
At least 100 people were drowned, and more
than 1.5 million were forced to flee their
homes.

Snow flakes as large as plates were observed at
Bratsk, in Siberia, in 1971. The largest
measured 8×12ins (200×300mm).

In January and February 1977, Buffalo, New
York, suffered blizzards which left snow drifts
20ft (6m) deep. These were compacted so hard
by the wind that the blades of several snow
ploughs were bent or even broken in attempts
to shift them.

The record for the heaviest snowfall over a
12-month period was set at Mount Rainier,
Washington, between 19 February 1972 and
18 February 1973, when 1,224.5ins (31,102mm)
of snow was recorded at the Paradise Ranger
Station. The heaviest fall in a single day was at
Silver Lake, Colorado, on 14-15 April 1921,
with 74ins (1,870mm). The deepest snow cover
on record was 27ft 7ins (8,407mm) at Helen
Lake, Mount Lassen in April 1983.

St Agnes Day, ah bitter chill it was,
The owl for all his feathers was so cold,
The hare limped trembling through the
frozen grass,
And silent stood the sheep in dusky fold.

The famous lines of John Keats reflect the fact that St Agnes Eve, 20 January, is reputedly the coldest day of the year in southern Britain. St Hilary's Day, 12 January, has the same reputation in the north.

If Candlemas Day is bright and clear,
There'll be two winters in that year;
But if Candlemas Day is mild or brings rain,
Winter is gone and will not come again.

Candlemas Day is 2 February and used to be regarded as being half-way through winter.

The North wind doth blow
And we shall have snow.

When the stars begin to huddle,
The earth will soon become a puddle.

When rain is approaching, refraction causes the smaller stars to look as if they are huddling in misty clusters.

When icicles hang by the wall
And Dick the shepherd blows his nail
And Tom bears logs into the hall
And milk comes frozen home in pail,
When blood is nipped and ways be foul,
Then nightly sings the staring owl,
Tu-whit, Tu-who! – a merry note,
While greasy Joan doth keel the pot.

William Shakespeare, 'Winter' from Love's Labour's Lost

The Thrushes and Blackbirds have been singing
me into an idea that it was Spring, and almost
that leaves were on the trees. So that black
clouds and boisterous winds seem to have
mustered and collected in full Divan, for the
purpose of convincing me to the contrary.

John Keats, Letter of 22 February 1818

Before the embankment was constructed beside
the River Thames in the nineteenth century,
London's wide and sluggish river often froze
over. In severe winters from the fifteenth to the
early nineteenth century, the period known as
the 'Little Ice Age', the ice was sometimes thick
enough for a Frost Fair, with shops, sideshows
and other activities including ox roasting on the
ice. In 1778 the river was frozen over for nine
weeks. The last Frost Fair took place for a few
days in 1814, when an elephant walked down
the Thames.

The most dismal winters in the world must be
those at the North Pole, which sees no sunshine
at all for 186 days.

The first person to photograph ice crystals with
a camera fitted to a microscope was William A.
Bentley (1865-1931), an American farmer who
went on to photograph over 6,000 different
crystals.

During a fierce blizzard in 1891 in Devon,
England, corn was reported to have germinated
and grown to a height of 3ins (75mm) beneath
the snow – the ground was warm when the
snow fell, and the snow would have had an
insulating effect against the cold air
temperature above.

The robin on my lawn
He was the first to tell
How, in the frozen dawn,
This miracle befell,
Waking the meadows white
With hoar, the iron road
Agleam with splintered light,
And ice where water flowed:
Till, when the low sun drank
Those milky mists that cloak
Hanger and hollied bank,
The winter world awoke
To hear the feeble bleat
Of lambs on the downland farms:
A blackbird whistled sweet;
Old beeches moved their arms
Into a mellow haze
Aerial; newly-born:
And I, alone, agaze,
Stood waiting for the thorn
To break in blossoms white,
Or burst in a green flame . . .
So, in a single night,
Fair February came,
Bidding my lips to sing
Or whisper their surprise,
With all the joy of spring
And morning in her eyes.

Francis Brett Young, 'February'

Moon and weather
May change together,
But a change of moon
Does not change the weather.

Either a halo or a corona around the moon on a winter night indicates rain or snow. A halo is seen when the moon shines through a veil of thin cloud, and is produced by the refraction of moonlight through ice crystals in the atmosphere. A corona, smaller in diameter, is produced, like a rainbow, by the refraction of light rays by water droplets in the cloud.

February brings the rain,
Melts the frozen lands again.

February fills dyke,
Thawing by day, freezing by night.

If in February there be no rain,
'Tis neither good for hay nor grain.

Red sky at night, shepherds delight;
Red sky in the morning, sailors take warning.

A clear reddish sky in the evening is usually followed by a fine day. White and red early morning sky foretells rain.

Therefore all seasons shall be sweet to thee,
Whether the summer clothe the general earth
With greenness, or the redbreast sit and sing
Betwixt the tufts of snow on the bare branch
Of mossy apple-tree, while the nigh thatch
Smokes in the sun-thaw; whether the
eave-drops fall
Heard only in the trances of the blast,
Or if the secret ministry of frost
Shall hang them up in silent icicles,
Quietly shining to the quiet Moon.

Samuel Taylor Coleridge